Plectrum Guitar
Grades 3-5

Pieces
for Trinity College London exams

Published by
Trinity College London
www.trinitycollege.com

Registered in England
Company no. 02683033
Charity no. 1014792

Barré Dance

Bryan Lester

Blue for a Day

Lee Sollory
(born 1959)

4

Tomorrow will be Better

Nick Powlesland
(born 1965)

Reproduced from *The Real Guitar Book* vol. 1, CM191

Tuesday Bluesday

Nick Powlesland
(born 1965)

* String bend and release

Turn to Dust

Nick Powlesland
(born 1965)

* A half bend at fret 2 may be substituted for the hammer-on.

Reproduced from *The Real Guitar Book* vol. 1, CM191

Valsetta

Richard Cobby

Ballade

Lee Sollory
(born 1959)

Reproduced from *The Real Guitar Book* vol. 2, CM192

Sun Song

Bryan Lester

Chillout

Nick Powlesland
(born 1965)

Étude no. 8

Gerald Garcia
(born 1949)

Mean Street

Nick Powlesland
(born 1965)

With attitude ♩ = 130

Summer Solstice Song

Lee Sollory
(born 1959)

One More Time

Roy Chilton
(born 1950)

N.B. pick 4th string with pick & 2nd string with 3rd finger

GRADE 5

Hazy Daze

Lee Sollory
(born 1959)

GRADE 5

Lonely Moments

Barney Kessel
(1923-2004)

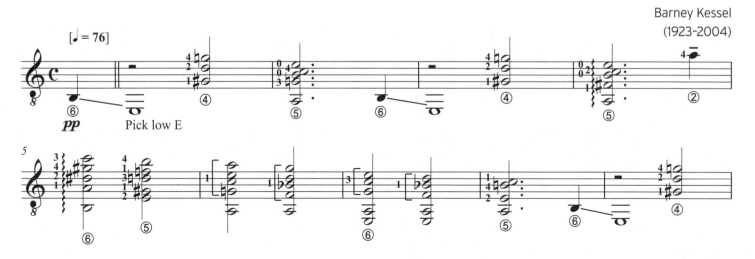

Rockroach

Nick Powlesland
(born 1965)

Short Poem

Bryan Lester

Song for Dorothy

Ben Crosland
(born 1968)